AUTHOR- JILLIA WEINBERGER

Dedicated by Jason and Asher Weinberger in loving memory of Jillia and her dream

DEDICATED TO
MY LITTLE ASH MONKEY,
THE GREATEST GIFT OF MY LIFE.

This Book Belongs to

NO PART OF THIS BOOK MAY BE REPRODUCED
IN ANY FORM WITHOUT WRITTEN
PERMISSION FROM THE PUBLISHER, EXCEPT FOR
BRIEF PASSAGES INCLUDED IN A REVIEW.

Early one summer morning, Mommy and Ash monkey were sitting in their treehouse. Mommy monkey had an idea. "Let's go on an adventure walk in the forest", she said. Ash monkey cheered with excitement as he raced to the front door to put on his shoes.

"For today's adventure, we are going to walk through the forest and use our five senses. We use our eyes to see, our ears to listen, our nose to smell, our mouth to taste and our hands to touch."

Ash monkey said "I see trees, and grass, and other animal families!". "Great job using your sense of sight, Ash", replied Mommy Monkey. "There are so many beautiful things we can see when we use our eyes to look".

They continued walking. Next, Ash heard a sweet sound and stopped to listen more clearly. "What do you hear?", asked Mommy. "I hear the birds chirping in the trees. If I am quiet and use my listening ears, I hear them singing their songs in the sky!". "That's right, Ash. There are so many sounds we can hear when we use our listening ears", said Mommy.

As they continued, Ash was so excited that he started running and tripped over a tree branch. As he sat on the floor, he noticed his hands touching the grass and dirt on the ground. "This is a great way to use your sense of touch, Ash. Tell me, how does it feel in your hands?", asked Mommy. "The grass feels soft and smooth and the dirt feels bumpy and hard", said Ash. "Excellent! You just used your sense of touch to tell me how the grass and dirt feel in your hands", said Mommy.

Next, they came upon a field of flowers. There were so many flowers. Some were white, some were pink, some were blue. Ash went up and started examining the flowers. "Use your nose to smell the flowers", said Mommy. Ash bent down and breathed in through his nose. "Wow, Mommy, these flowers smell so nice! Hey, I just used my sense of smell!". "Yes you did, Ash", said Mommy.

As they headed back towards the treehouse, it started to rain. Big, wet raindrops fell from the sky. Ash opened his mouth to catch the drops. "Tastes like water", he said to Mommy. Mommy opened her mouth to catch some rain too. "You're right! It does taste like the water we drink at home! You just used your sense of taste."

The day was over and it was almost time for bed. The monkeys got back to their treehouse from their big adventure. "This was so much fun Mommy! I loved exploring the forest and using all my senses. Let's do it again!". "Tomorrow, baby", she said. "Mommy needs to sleep first so we can have another fun adventure tomorrow."

"Goodnight mommy", said Ash.
"Goodnight baby", said Mommy.

CONTACT US

EMAIL: JILLIA.WEINB@GMAIL.COM

INSTAGRAM: MOMMYLIFEFUN

Made in the USA
Middletown, DE
22 October 2022

13243607R00015